CW00349767

Time Pieces

for
Trombone

𝄞 and 𝄢

Music through the Ages in Two Volumes

Volume 1

Paul Harris and Amos Miller

Perry Pieces
£ 4.75

The Associated Board of
the Royal Schools of Music

CONTENTS

Time Pieces for Trombone

Volume 1

for David and Ida Miller

*c.*1250 Sumer is icumen in

Anon.

© 2001 by The Associated Board of the Royal Schools of Music

AB 2788

1415   Agincourt Song

Anon.

1595   Now is the month of maying

Thomas Morley
(1557–1602)

1691   Fairest Isle

from *King Arthur*

Henry Purcell
(1659–1695)

AB 2788

1710 Wer hat dich so geschlagen

from *St Matthew Passion*

Moderato ♩ = 80

Trombone

Piano

1726 Sarabande

from *Six solos for a Violin and Base with a*
Through Base for the Harpsichord

John Humphries
(1707–1773)

AB 2788

1760 Largo andante

from No. 8 of *Eight Symphonys*, Op. 2

William Boyce
(1711–1779)

*c.*1800 **The Blue Bells of Scotland**

Traditional

1812 Equale No. 1

Ludwig van Beethoven
(1770–1827)

AB 2788

1848 Andante con moto

from *50 leçons*, Op. 9

Giuseppe Concone
(1801–1861)

AB 2788

*c.*1860 Go Down Moses

(Spiritual)

Anon.

AB 2788

1868 Lullaby

Op. 49 No. 4

Johannes Brahms
(1833–1897)

1878 Captain Corcoran's Song

Sir Arthur Sullivan
(1842–1900)

from *HMS Pinafore*

AB 2788

1894 Romance

Arnold Dolmetsch
(1858–1940)

from *Pieces for Cello*

AB 2788

1896 To a Wild Rose

from *Woodland Sketches*

Edward MacDowell
(1860–1908)

AB 2788

1900 Canción

Manuel de Falla
(1876–1946)

1934 La ceinture de noces

from *Vingt chansons bretonnes*

Charles Koechlin
(1867–1950)

Reproduced by permission of Editions Salabert, Paris/United Music Publishers Ltd.

1945 Autumn Leaves

Joseph Kosma (1905–1969)
Words by Johnny Mercer
(after Jacques Prevert)

© 1947 Enoch & Cie and Ardmore Music Corp. Peter Maurice Music Co. Ltd, London WC2H 0QY
Reproduced by permission of IMP Ltd. All rights reserved.

1946 Play

from *For Children*, Vol. 1

Béla Bartók
(1881–1945)

NEW REVISED EDITION © Copyright 1946 by Boosey & Hawkes Inc. Sole agents for Benelux states, British Commonwealth, France, Italy, Portugal, Scandinavian states, Spain, Switzerland, UK & USA: Boosey & Hawkes Music Publishers Ltd. For all other countries: Editio Musica Budapest. This edition © Copyright 1998 by Boosey & Hawkes Music Publishers Ltd/Editio Musica Budapest. This arrangement © 2001 by Boosey & Hawkes Music Publishers Ltd.

2001 Funny Bone

Paul Harris

© 2001 by The Associated Board of the Royal Schools of Music

Music origination by
Barnes Music Engraving Ltd, East Sussex
Printed in England by Caligraving Ltd, Thetford, Norfolk

AB 2788